50 NEW ANTHEMS
FOR MIXED VOICES

We hope you enjoy the music in this book. Further copies are available from your local music shop or Christian bookshop.

In case of difficulty, please contact the publisher direct by writing to:

The Sales Department
KEVIN MAYHEW LTD
Buxhall
Stowmarket
Suffolk IP14 3BW

Phone 01449 737978
Fax 01449 737834
E-mail info@kevinmayhewltd.com

Please ask for our complete catalogue of outstanding Church Music.

First published in Great Britain in 1999 by Kevin Mayhew Ltd.

© Copyright 1999 Kevin Mayhew Ltd.

ISBN 1 84003 431 9
ISMN M 57004 596 9
Catalogue No: 1450146

0 1 2 3 4 5 6 7 8 9

Cover design by Jaquetta Sergeant

Music Editor and Setter: Donald Thomson
Proof-reader: Kate Gallaher

Printed and bound in Great Britain

50 NEW ANTHEMS
FOR MIXED VOICES

Kevin
Mayhew

Contents

A GAELIC BENEDICTION

Text: Fiona MacLeod (1855-1905)
Music: Brian Glading (b.1931)

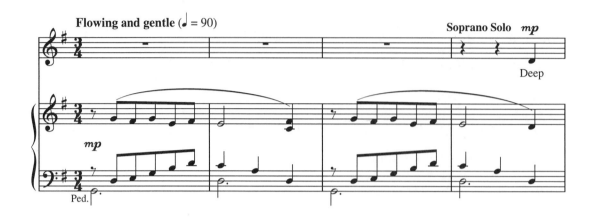

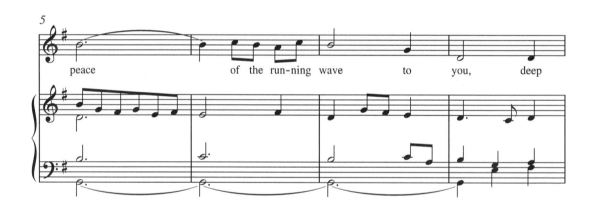

peace of the qui-et earth to you, deep

peace of the qui-et earth to you.

Deep

peace of the run-ning wave to you, deep

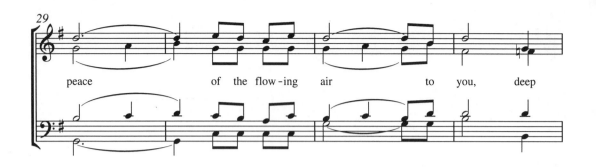

peace   of the flow -ing air   to   you, deep

peace   of the qui - et earth   to   you, deep

peace   of the qui - et earth   to you, deep

peace   of the gen - tle night   to   you, deep

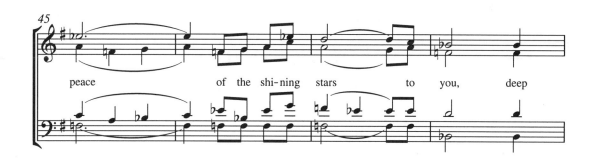

peace of the shi-ning stars to you, deep

peace of the Son of Peace to you, deep

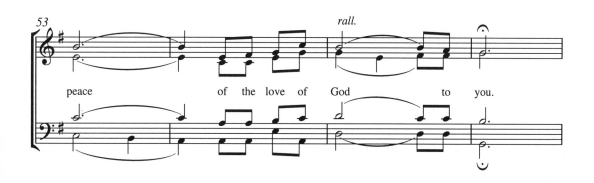

peace of the love of God to you.

9

To the Reverend Canon H. Kilworth Maybury
and the Choir of St. John's Episcopal Church, Portage, Wisconsin

A HYMN OF THANKSGIVING

Text: Michael Forster (b.1946)
Music: William Lloyd Webber (1914-1982)

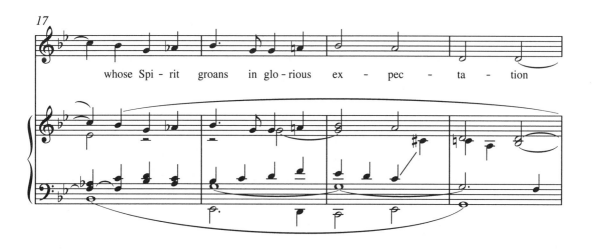

whose Spi - rit groans in glo - rious ex - pec - ta - tion

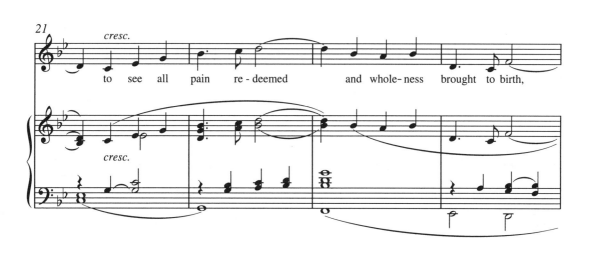

to see all pain re - deemed and whole - ness brought to birth,

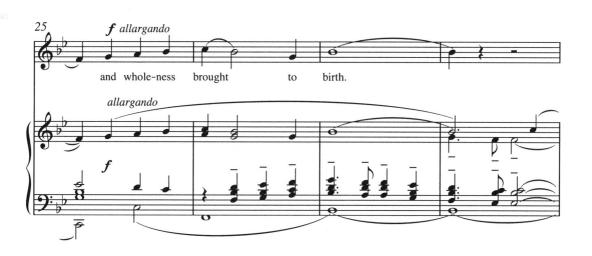

and whole-ness brought to birth.

Glo - ry to God, the bear - er of sal - va - tion, whose pre - sence bless'd with life Man. the Vir - gin's womb, who, by the won - der of the in - car - na - tion, made hu - man life di - vine

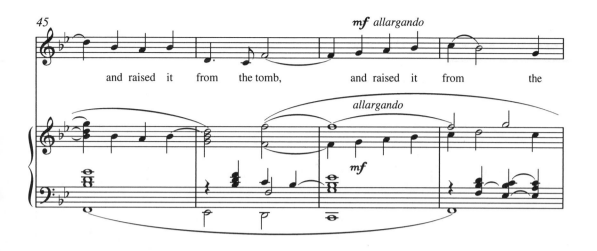

and raised it from the tomb, and raised it from the

tomb.

Glo - ry to God from ev - 'ry race and

Glo - ry to God from ev - 'ry race and

ALLELUIA

Text: from Scripture
Music: Noel Rawsthorne (b.1929)

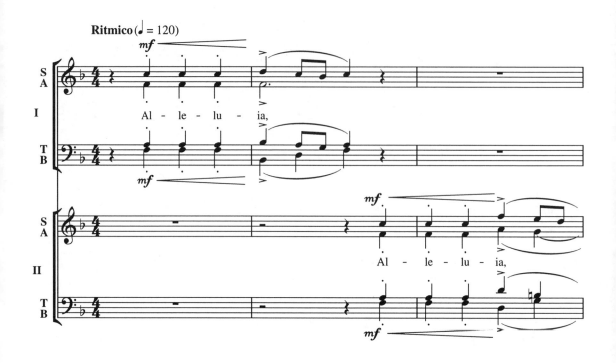

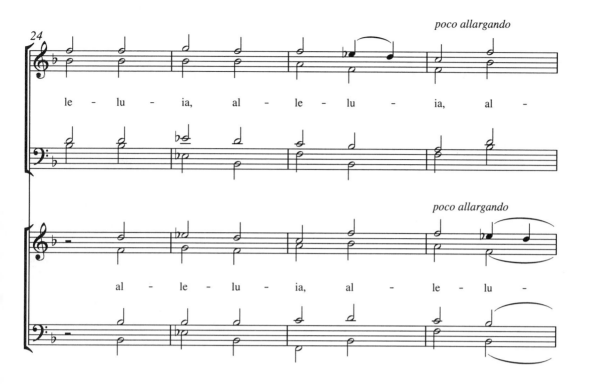

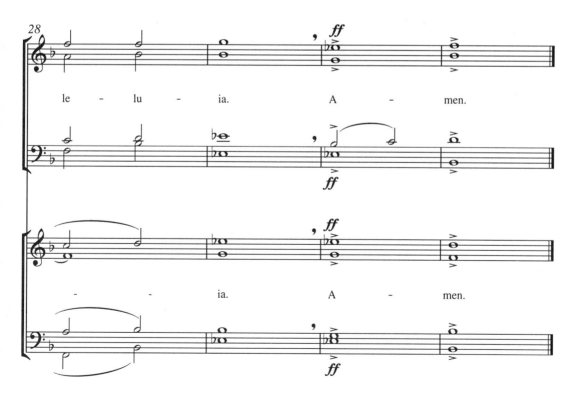

19

ALLELUIA! CHRIST IS RISEN

Text: Michael Forster (b.1946)
Music: Stephen Kemp (b.1947)

Christ is ri - sen, whom the grave could not con - fine.

We pro - claim the hope e - ter - nal, spring - ing out of

love di - vine. Al - le - lu - ia! Al - le - lu - ia!

Ce – le- brate with bread and wine!

div. **mf**

Al – le – lu – ia! Christ is ri – sen!

div. **mf**

mf

He ful – fills our dee- pest need: need: out of sla – v'ry

into freedom, all cre-a-tion will he lead.

Al - le - lu - ia! Al - le - lu - ia! This our hope, our

joy, our creed.

23

50 NEW ANTHEMS
FOR MIXED VOICES

AND NOW, O FATHER, MINDFUL OF THE LOVE

Text: William Bright (1824-1901)
Music: Richard Lloyd (b.1933)

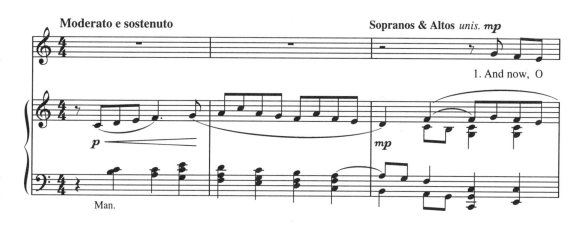

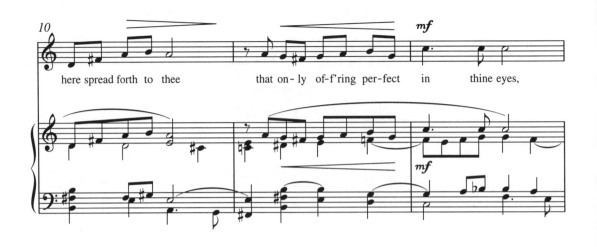

here spread forth to thee   that on- ly of-f'ring per-fect   in   thine eyes,

the one true, pure, im- mor- tal   sa -   cri- fice.

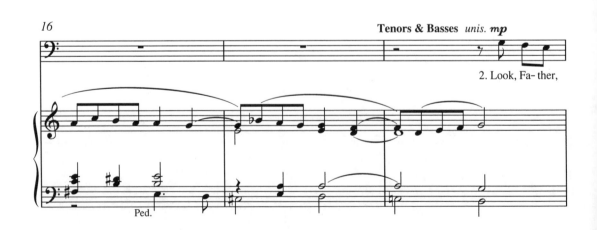

Tenors & Basses *unis.* **mp**

2. Look, Fa- ther,

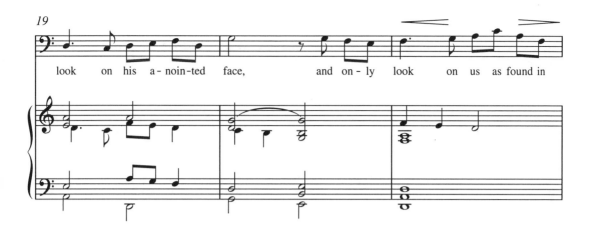

look on his a- noin-ted face, and on-ly look on us as found in

him; look not on our mis-u-sings of thy grace, our pray'r so lan-guid

and our faith so dim; for lo, be-tween our sins and their re-ward

from taint-ing
for their souls' true weal; from taint-ing mis-chief keep them white and clear,

and crown thy gifts with strength to per - se -vere.

4. And so we come; O draw us to thy feet, most pa -tient
unis.

and grant us ne - ver - more to part

with thee.

A PRAYER ON THE COMPOSER'S 60TH BIRTHDAY

Text: inscription on the clock at Chester Cathedral
Music: Colin Mawby (b.1936)

When as a child I laughed and wept – Time crept,

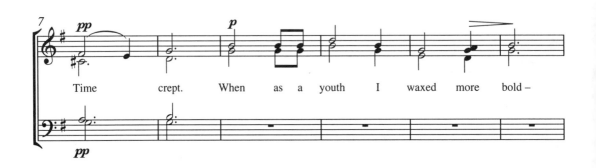

Time crept. When as a youth I waxed more bold –

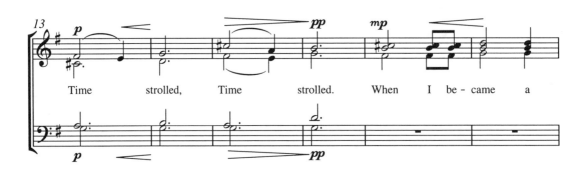

Time strolled, Time strolled. When I be-came a

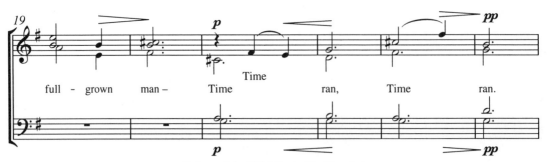

full - grown man – Time ran, Time ran.

When   ol – der   still   I   grew –   Time   flew,

Time   flew,   flew,

Time   Time   flew.   Soon   I   shall   find   in   pas – sing

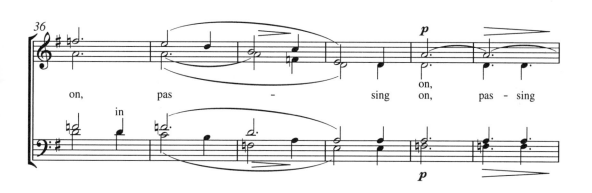

on,   pas   –   sing   on,   pas – sing

in

on –   Time   gone,   Time   gone.   O

Christic, will thou have saved me then –

For John and Jill

AVE VERUM CORPUS

Text: 14th Century
Music: Colin Mawby (b.1936)

O Je - su dul - cis! O
O Je - su dul - cis! O
O Je - su dul - cis! O
O Je - su dul - cis! O

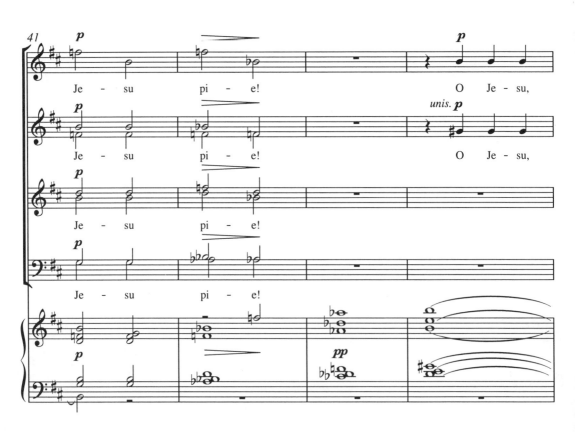

Je - su pi - e! O Je - su,
Je - su pi - e! O Je - su,
Je - su pi - e!
Je - su pi - e!

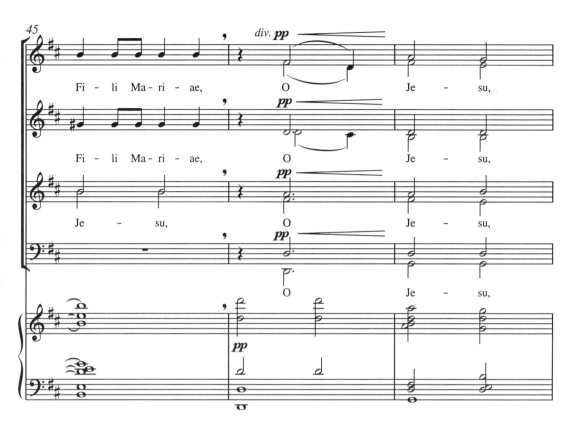

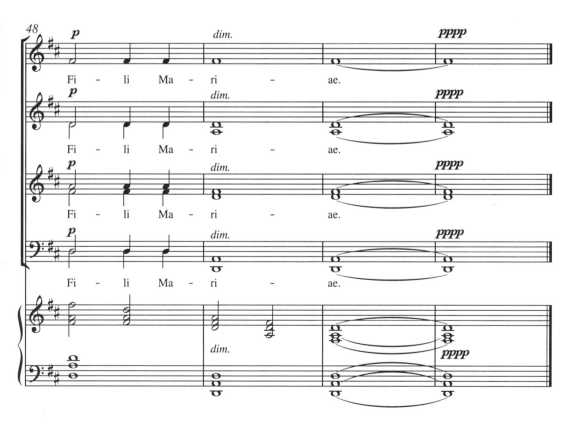

43

50 NEW ANTHEMS
FOR MIXED VOICES

BE THOU MY GUARDIAN AND MY GUIDE

Text: Isaac Williams (1802-1865)
Music: David Terry (b.1975)

flesh, and Sa – tan dwell a – round the paths I tread; O

O save me from the snares of hell, thou quick – 'ner

47

Lord, keep watch with-in, and save my soul from wrong.

ah.

ah. Still

ah. Still

ah. Still

let me e-ver watch and pray, and feel that I am

let me e-ver watch and pray, and feel that I am

let me e-ver watch and pray, and feel that I am

let me e-ver watch and pray, and feel that I am

frail, that if the temp - ter cross my way, yet

frail, that if the temp - ter cross my way, yet

frail, that if the temp - ter cross my way, yet

frail, that if the temp - ter cross my way, yet

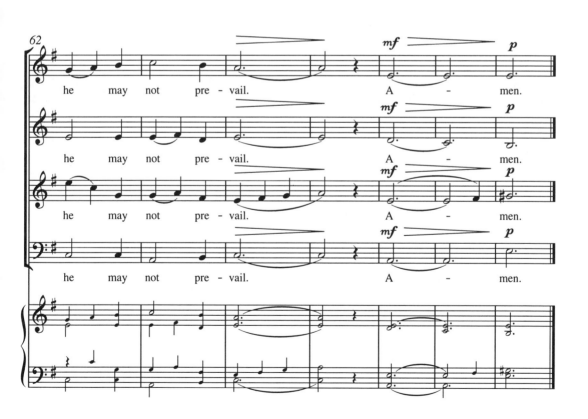

he may not pre - vail. A - men.

he may not pre - vail. A - men.

he may not pre - vail. A - men.

he may not pre - vail. A - men.

BLESSED ARE THE PURE IN HEART

Text: vs. 1 & 3, John Keble (1792-1866); vs. 2 & 4, John Hall alt.
Music: Malcolm Archer (b.1952)

Lord who left the heav'ns our life and
Lord who left the heav'ns our life and
Lord who left the heav'ns our life and
Lord who left the heav'ns our life and

peace to bring, to dwell in low - li -
peace to bring, to dwell in low - li -
peace to bring, to dwell in low - li -
peace to bring, to dwell in low - li -

51

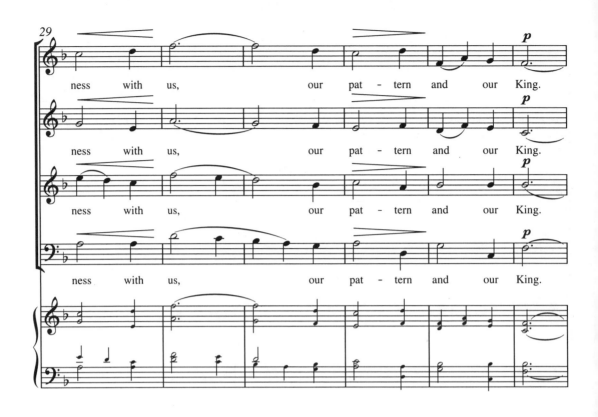

ness with us, our pat - tern and our King.

ness with us, our pat - tern and our King.

ness with us, our pat - tern and our King.

ness with us, our pat - tern and our King.

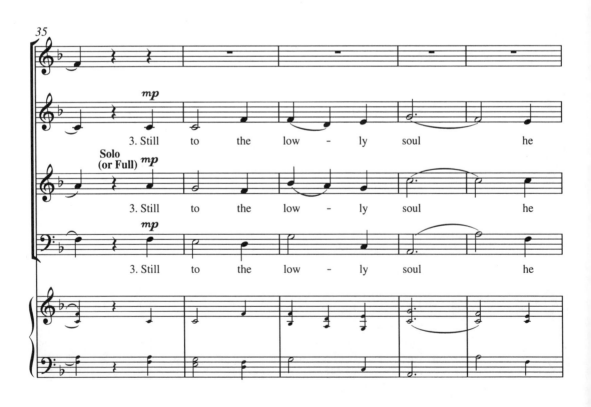

3. Still to the low - ly soul he

Solo (or Full) 3. Still to the low - ly soul he

3. Still to the low - ly soul he

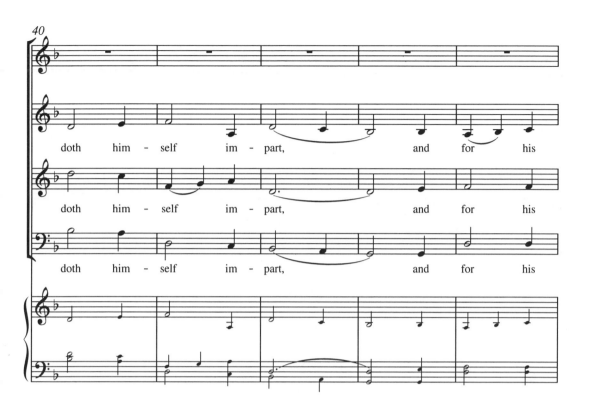

doth him - self im - part, and for his

doth him - self im - part, and for his

doth him - self im - part, and for his

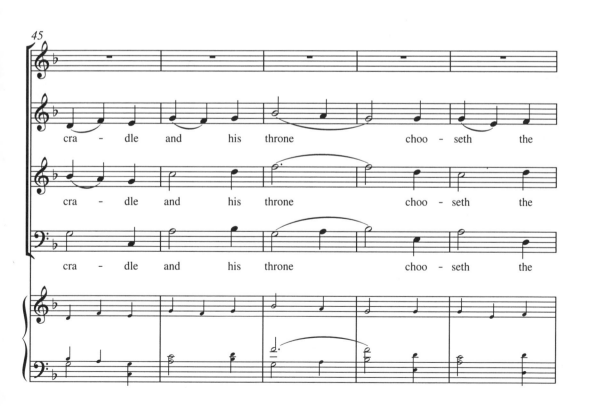

cra - dle and his throne choo - seth the

cra - dle and his throne choo - seth the

cra - dle and his throne choo - seth the

4. Lord, we thy pre - sence seek, may ours this bles - sing be:

pure in heart. Ah,

pure in heart. Ah,

pure in heart.

ah,

ah,

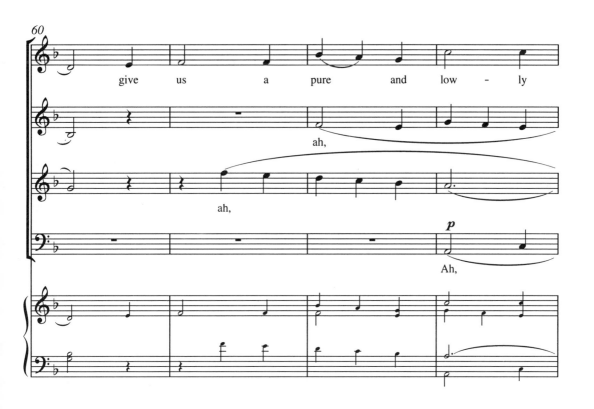

give us a pure and low - ly

ah,

ah,

Ah,

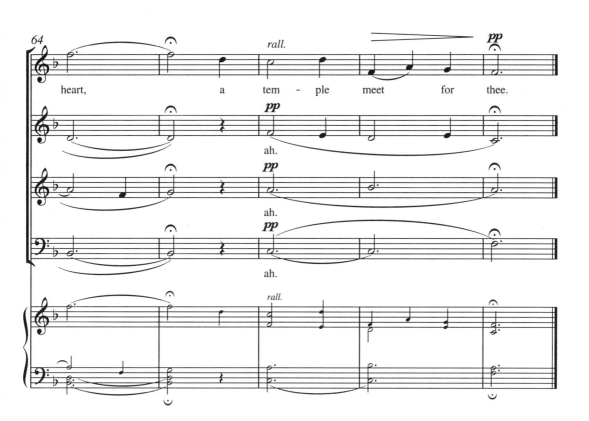

heart, a tem - ple meet for thee.

ah.

ah.

ah.

55

BLESS THE LORD, MY SOUL

Text: from Psalm 103
Music: Andrew Moore (b.1954)

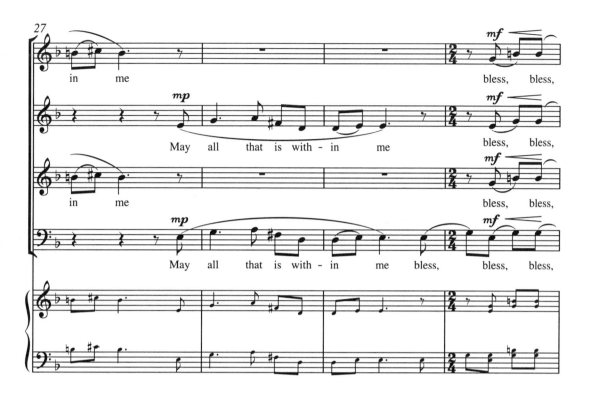

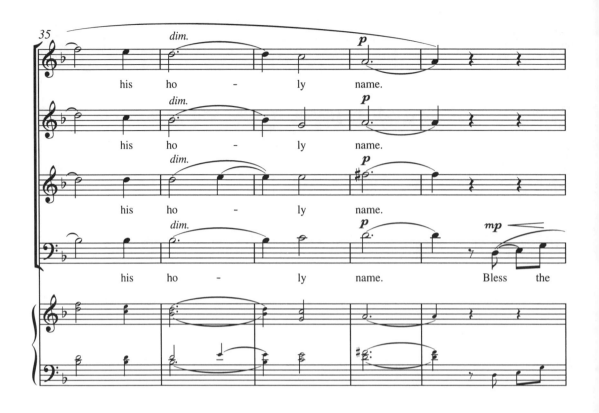

his ho - ly name.
his ho - ly name.
his ho - ly name.
his ho - ly name. Bless the

bless the Lord, my soul, bless the
Lord, my soul, my soul, bless the

50 NEW ANTHEMS
FOR MIXED VOICES

BREAD OF HEAVEN, ON THEE WE FEED

Text: Reginald Heber (1783-1826)
Music: Malcolm Archer (b.1952)

bread, day by day with strength sup - plied through the life of him who died.

Vine of heav'n, thy blood sup - plies this blest cup of sa - cri - fice; 'tis thy wounds our heal-ing give; to thy

cross we look and live: thou our life! O let us be root-ed,

graft - ed, built on thee. A -

Man.

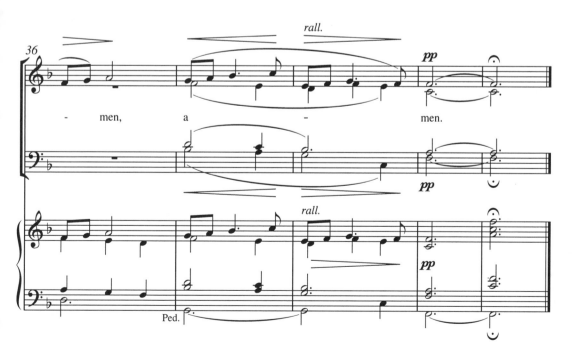

- men, a - men.

Ped.

BREAD OF HEAVEN, ON THEE WE FEED

Text: Josiah Conder (1789-1855)
Music: Richard Lloyd (b.1933)

this blest cup of sa - cri - fice; 'tis thy wounds our heal - ing give,

to thy Cross we look and live: thou our life! O let us be

root - ed, graft - ed, built in thee, root - ed, graft - ed, built in thee.

For Martin Schellenberg and the Choir of Christchurch Priory
during the 900th anniversary celebration of the Priory

CHRIST IS OUR CORNERSTONE

Text: translated from the Latin by J. Chandler (1806-1876)
Music: Malcolm Archer (b.1952)

This anthem is also available separately with parts for trumpets and timpani.

his great love our hopes we place of pre-sent grace and joys a-

bove.

* Sopranos *mf*

O then with hymns of praise these

dim.

* or SA at conductor's discretion

hal - lowed courts shall ring; our voi - ces we will raise the

Three in One to sing; and thus pro - claim in joy - ful song, both

loud and long, that glo - rious name.

Tpt.

mp

71

Here, gra- cious God, do thou for e - ver- more draw

nigh; ac - cept each faith- ful vow, and mark each sup - pliant

sigh; in co- pious show'r on all who pray each ho - ly day thy

bles - sings pour.

Here may we gain from heav'n the

grace which we im - plore; and may that grace, once giv'n, be

with us e - ver - more, un -

Tpt.

til that day when all the blest, un - til that day when all the blest, un -

COME, DEAREST LORD

Text: Isaac Watts (1674-1748)
Music: Richard Lloyd (b.1933)

77

COME, YE THANKFUL PEOPLE, COME

Text: Henry Alford (1810-1871)
Music: Michael Rose (b.1934)

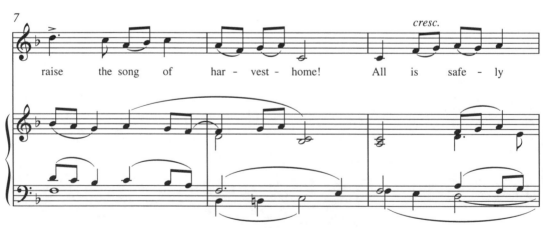

ga - thered in, ere the win – ter storms be - gin;

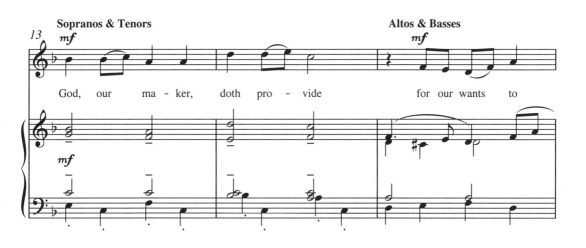

Sopranos & Tenors

Altos & Basses

God, our ma - ker, doth pro - vide for our wants to

All

be sup - plied; come to God's own tem - ple, come;

praise to yield; wheat and tares to - ge - ther sown,

un - to joy or sor - row grown; first the blade and

then the ear, then the full corn shall ap - pear:

um - phant, come, raise the song of har - vest - home;

cresc.

all be safe - ly ga - thered in, free from sor - row,

free from sin, there for e - ver pu - ri - fied

in God's gar - ner to a - bide: come, ten thou - sand

an - gels, come, raise the song, raise the song,

raise the glo - rious har - vest, har - vest -

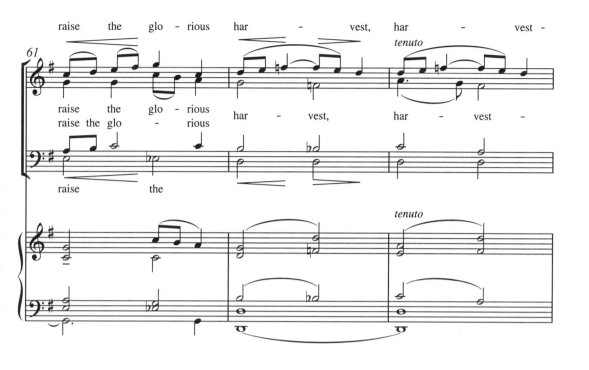

raise the glo - rious har - vest, har - vest -
raise the glo - rious har - vest, har - vest -

raise the

tenuto

a tempo
home!

home!

Full

a tempo *rall.*

DANCE, MY HEART

Text: Kabir, the Mystic Weaver trans. Rabindranath Tagore (1861-1941)
Music: Malcolm Archer (b.1952)

joy! The hymn of love fill – eth the days and the nights with mu – sic. And the world hear – ken – eth to the me – lo – dy.

Ped.

Man.

Why put on the robe of a monk and live a - loof from the world in lone - ly pride?

ah,

ah,

in   lone - ly   pride?

ah.

poco a poco stringendo

poco a poco stringendo

Full Sw. *mp*

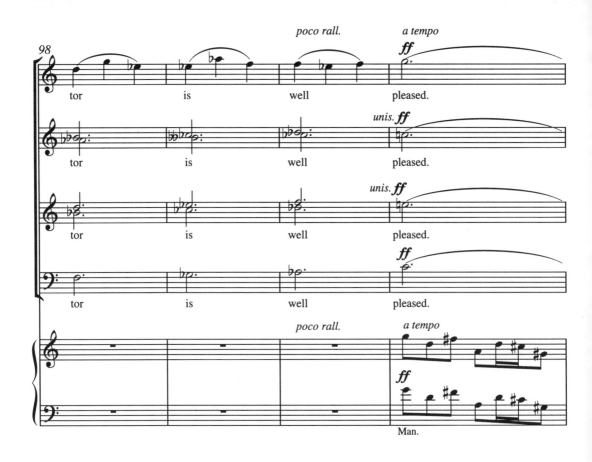

tor is well pleased.

tor is well pleased.

tor is well pleased.

tor is well pleased.

DAY BY DAY

Text: St Richard of Chichester
Music: Norman Warren (b.1934)

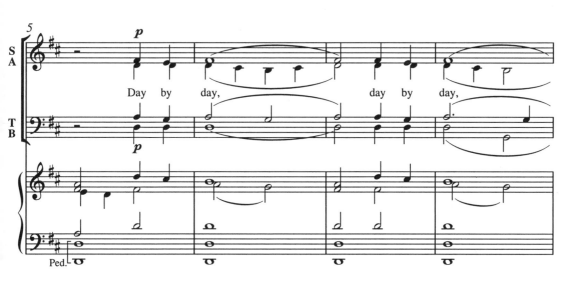

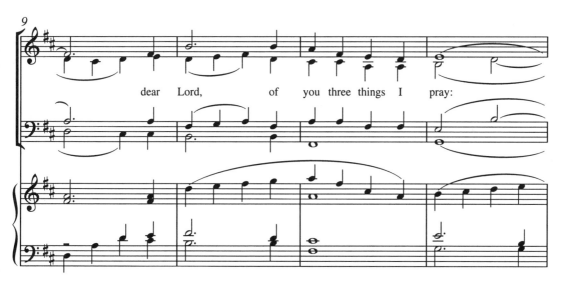

to see you more clear - ly, to love you more

dear - ly, to fol - low you more near - ly, day by

day. To see you more clear - ly, to love you more

dear - ly, to fol - low you more near - ly   day by

day,   day by day.

DEEP WITHIN ME

Text: The Very Rev. The Hon. Hugh Dickinson (b.1929)
Music: Michael Higgins (b.1981)

3. Clothe me in your Spirit's love; let your shi-ning ne-ver cease; let my spi-rit al-ways move in the ra-di-ance of peace.

DOMINUS FIRMAMENTUM MEUM

Text: Psalm 17 (18):3
Music: William Lloyd Webber (1914-1982)

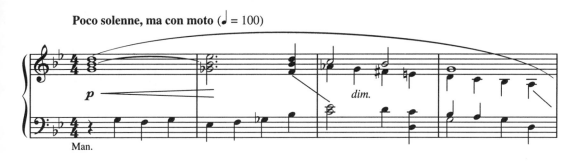

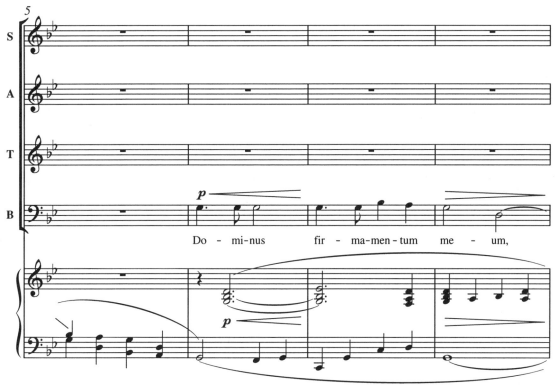

Translation: The Lord is my stronghold and my refuge,
and my deliverer. My God is my help.

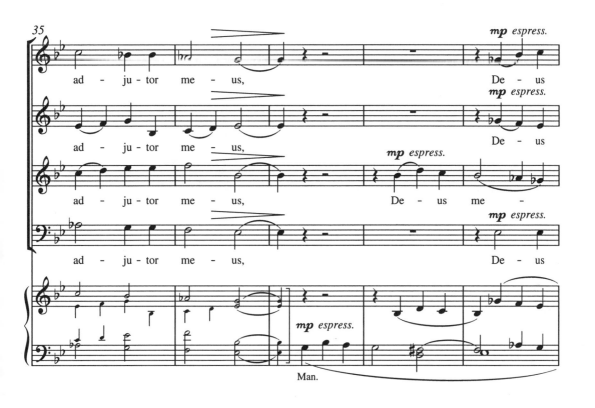

107

For Richard Seal

EXULTET: REJOICE, O HEAVENLY POWERS

Text: from the Easter Liturgy
Music: Malcolm Archer (b.1952)

Sound the trum - pet of sal - va - tion.

Re -

joice, O earth in shi - ning splen - dour, ra - diant in the

bright - ness of our King! Christ has con - quered, glo - ry

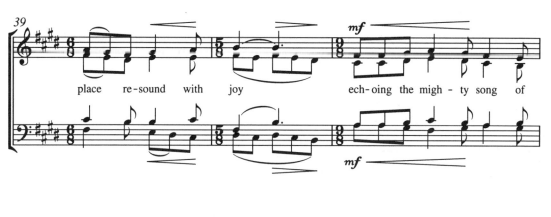

place re-sound with joy ech-oing the migh - ty song of

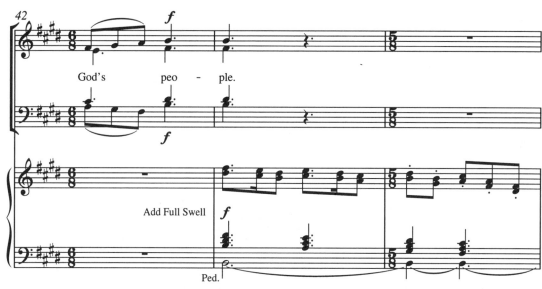

God's peo - ple.

Add Full Swell

Ped.

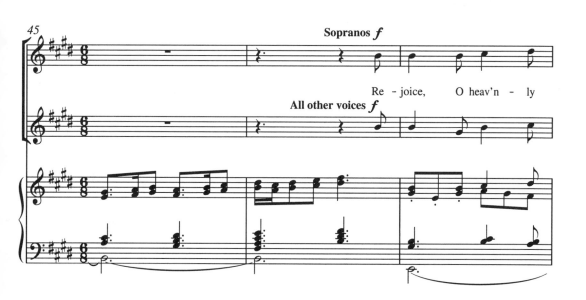

Sopranos *f*

Re - joice, O heav'n - ly

All other voices *f*

pow'rs! Sing choirs of an - gels! Ex - ult all cre -

a - tion a - round God's throne! Je - sus Christ our King is

ri - sen! Sound the trum - pet of sal - va - tion.

FOUNTAIN OF LIFE

Text: Michael Forster (b.1946)
Music: Margaret Rizza (b.1929)

Verses

1. Pre - serve and keep me all my days, in
2. Lord, lead me out and guide me in. Pro -

good in - tent and faith - ful ways. And lead me to such
tect me both from fear and sin. En - fold me in such your

ho - li - ness as mor - tal pray'rs can - not ex - press. O
con - stant love, with grace a - bun - dant from a - bove. O

3. Be there to guide me when I speak, to streng - then when my love is weak; be

D.S.

there to calm my fi - nal breath, and light the way to life through death. O

Dm⁷   G⁷/F   Em⁷   Am   Dm⁷   G   Csus⁴   C

S foun - tain of life, O foun - tain of life, O foun - tain of life, O

A Of life, of life,

T B Of life,

Optional accompaniment

foun - tain of life, O foun - tain of life, O foun - tain of life, O

of life, of life, of life,

foun - tain of life, foun - tain of

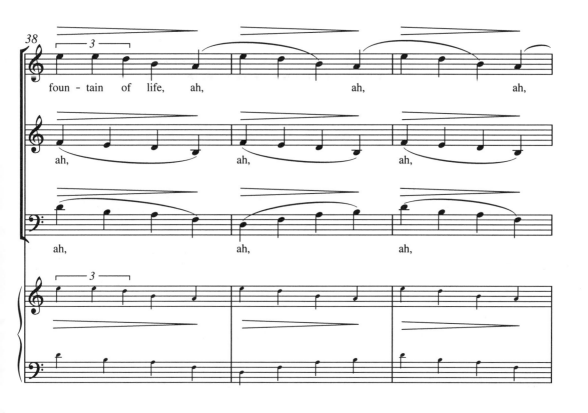

foun - tain of life, ah, ah, ah,

ah, ah, ah,

ah, ah, ah,

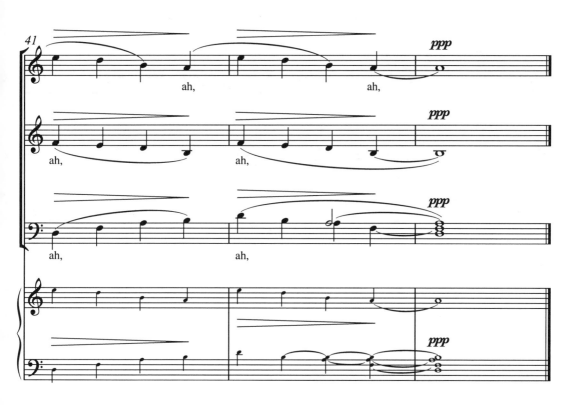

ah, ah, *ppp*

ah, ah, *ppp*

ah, ah, *ppp*

ppp

HYMN OF ST PATRICK

Text: from 'The Hymn of St Patrick' trans. Cecil Frances Alexander (1818-1895)
Music: Margaret Rizza (b.1929)

Christ in hearts of all that love me, Christ in mouth of friend and stran - ger. Christ be with me, Christ with - in me, Christ be with me, Christ with - in me, Christ with - in me, Christ with - in me, Christ with - in me.

IN THE BEGINNING WAS THE WORD OF LIFE

Text: Michael Forster (b.1946)
Music: Rosalie Bonighton (b.1946)

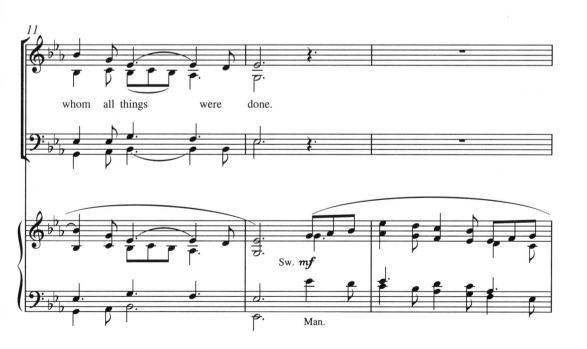

the Word of life,
cresc.

There in the dark - ness was the Word, the Word of life, with light for

the Word of life,

hu - man - kind.

Still un - de - fea - ted is the Word of

a - tion came the Word of life to those who were his own;

the Word of life

scorned and re - jec - ted, still the Word, the Word of life made love e -

the Word of life

126

JESUS, YOU ARE THE WAY

Text: Pamela Hayes
Music: Margaret Rizza (b.1929)

way that I can see all the Fa - ther means to me.

Je - su, Je - su, Je - su,

Je - sus, you are the way I can be - gin to let the Spi - rit breathe with -

Je - su, Je - su, Je - su,

in. Je - sus, my wea - ry head has found its rest in the

Je - su, Je - su, Je - su,

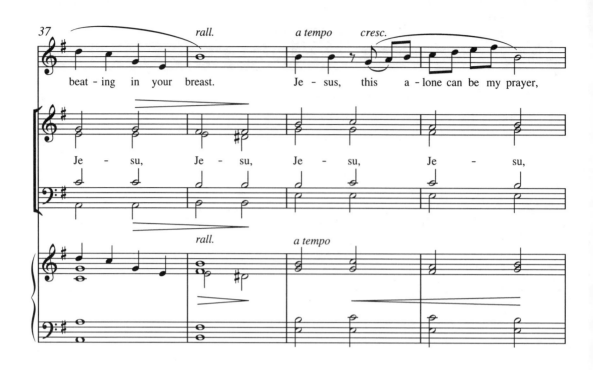

beat-ing in your breast. Je - sus, this a - lone can be my prayer,

Je - su, Je - su, Je - su, Je - su,

you are the way, your pierced heart o - pen there.

Je - su, Je - su, Je - su,

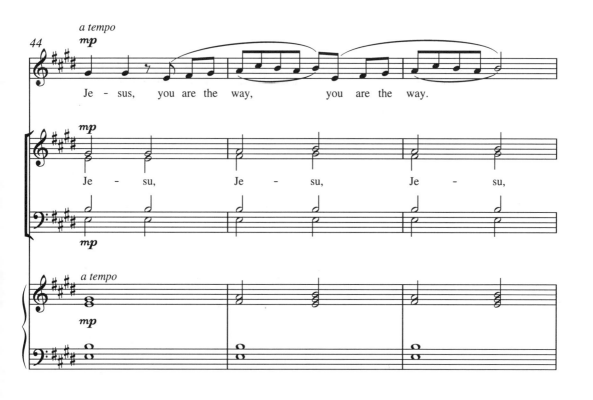

131

Composed for the dedication of the newly restored Father Willis organ
on 27th July 1997 at St. Mary's, North Leigh, Oxon.

LET MY DUE FEET NEVER FAIL TO WALK

Text: John Milton (1608-1674)
Music: Peter Irving (b.1959)

Let my due feet ne - ver fail to walk the stu - dious

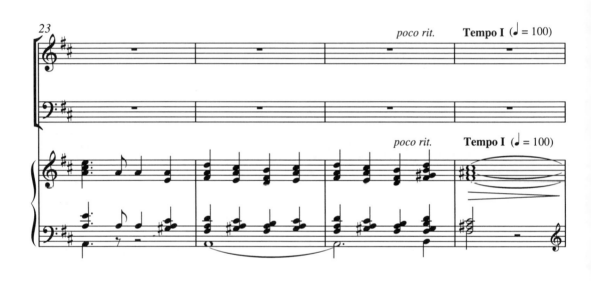

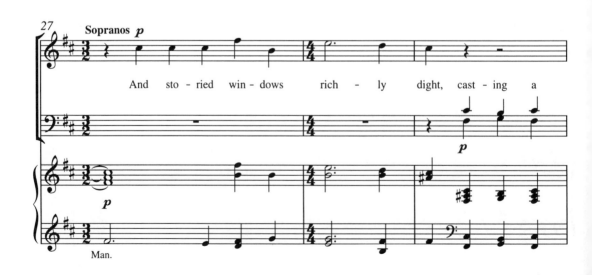

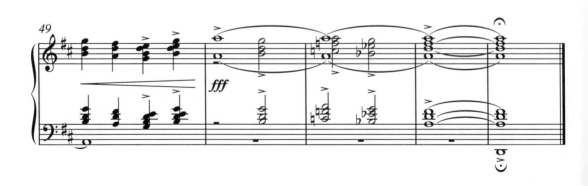

LET US, WITH A GLADSOME MIND

Text: John Milton (1608-1674) based on Psalm 135
Music: Martin Setchell (b.1949)

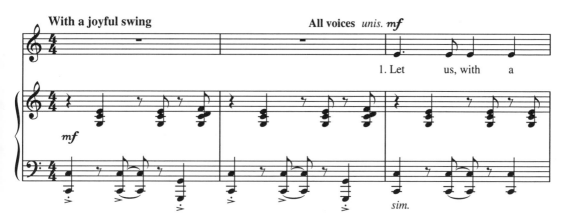

Accompaniment is for piano

138

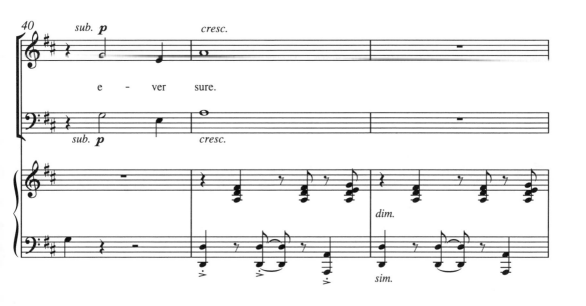

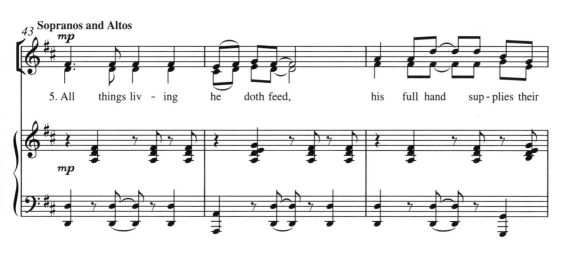

5. All things liv - ing he doth feed, his full hand sup - plies their

need; for his mer - cies aye en - dure,

dure,   e – ver faith - ful,   e – ver faith - ful,

e –   ver   sure.

143

50 NEW ANTHEMS
FOR MIXED VOICES

For James A. Person, in celebration of seventeen years of music ministry at Church of Our Saviour, San Gabriel, California by the Ella T. Person Memorial Fund.

LIGHT'S ABODE, CELESTIAL SALEM

Text: 15th century Latin trans. John Mason Neale (1818-1866)
Music: Malcolm Archer (b.1952)

145

is the feast day of the Lord; all is pure and all is ho - ly

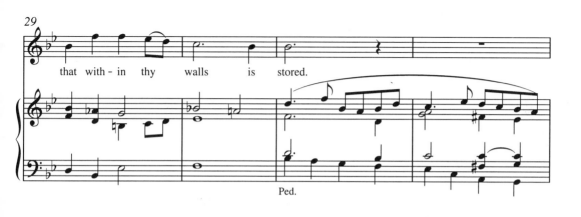

that with - in thy walls is stored.

Ped.

O, how glo - rious and re - splen - dent,

O, how glo - rious and re - splen - dent,

O, how glo - rious and re - splen - dent,

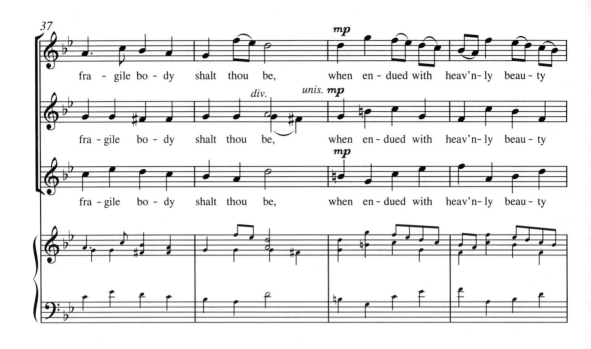

on thee laid, that here - af - ter these thy la - bours

may with end - less gifts be paid, and in e - ver -

last - ing glo - ry thou with bright - ness be ar -

150

LIKE AS THE HART

Text: from Psalm 42
Music: Noel Rawsthorne (b.1929)

that shall keep my soul. My

tears have been my meat day and night, while they dai - ly say un - to

me, where is now thy God, where is now thy God?

Like as the hart de -

Like as the

155

50 NEW ANTHEMS
FOR MIXED VOICES

For Rev. Keith Matthews

LITTLE LAMB, WHO MADE THEE?

Text: William Blake (1757-1827)
Music: Martin Setchell (b.1949)

feed by the stream and o'er the mead, gave thee such a ten-der

voice, ma-king all the vales re - joice?

Lit - tle Lamb, who made thee? Dost thou know who made thee?

Man.

2. Lit - tle Lamb, I'll tell thee, lit - tle Lamb, I'll tell thee.

He is cal - led by thy

Soprano Solo (or Full)

Man.

159

28

name for he calls him - self a lamb, he is meek and he is

31

mild, he be - came a lit - tle child,

34

I a child, and thou a lamb, we are cal - led by his

Lit - tle Lamb, God bless thee, lit - tle

name.

Lamb, God bless thee!

LORD OF THE HARVEST

Text: adapted from Genesis: 8, 9; Psalm 107:31
Music: Colin Hand (b.1929)

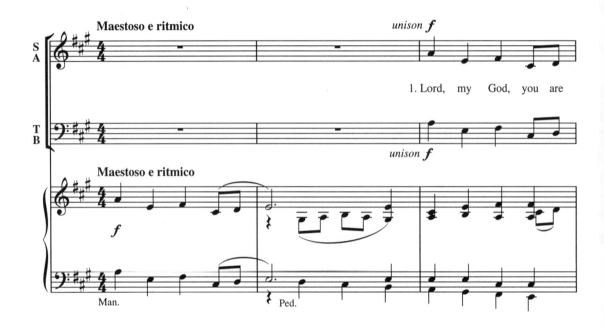

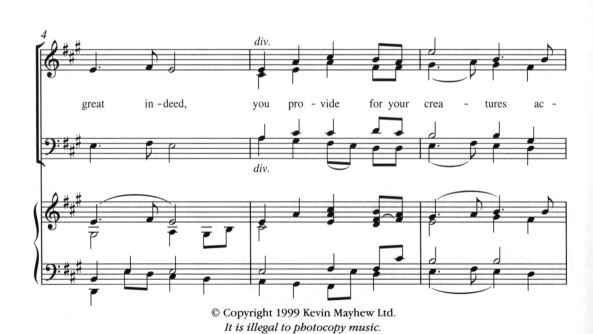

cor - ding to their needs. For the glo - ry of the Lord stands for

e - ver, and the Lord shall re -joice in his works.

You pro - mised your own ser - vant, Noah, that

while the earth re - mains, the har - vest ne - ver shall

cease. For the glo - ry of the Lord stands for e - ver, and the

Lord shall re - joice in his works.

Basses *mf*

You

Man.

send forth the Win – ter frosts to break up the ground for the

Ped.

mf

you send forth the show'rs in the Spring to

so – wer;

nur – ture the new – sown seed.

Tenors *mf*

You

send forth the Sum - mer sun to ri - pen the swel - ling

then the earth brings forth its yield and the

grain;

needs of folk are met. Count-less are the gifts be -

stowed, O Lord, gifts be-stowed in your wis – dom so that

earth is sa – tis – fied. For the glo – ry of the Lord stands for

e – ver, and the Lord shall re –joice in his works.

50 NEW ANTHEMS
FOR MIXED VOICES

LORD, WHEN I WAKE

Text: Brian Foley (b.1919)
Music: John Marsh (b.1939)

13 **Sopranos** *p*

I live with ma - ny in our world – their world - ly eyes too

p

Man.

17

blind to see who ne - ver think what is your will, or

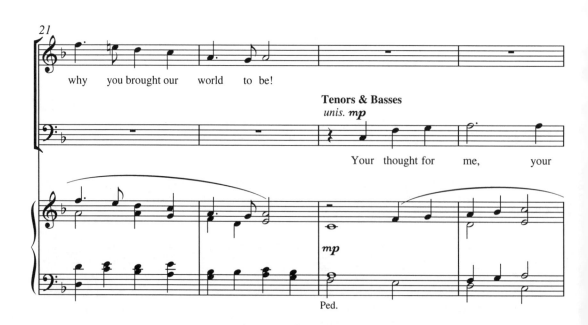

21

why you brought our world to be!

Tenors & Basses
unis. **mp**

Your thought for me, your

mp

Ped.

loving care those favours I could never

earn, call for my thanks in praise and prayer.

Call me to love you in return.

There is no bles-sing, Lord, from you for those who make their

no praise

will their way, no praise for those who do not praise, no

peace for those who do not pray.

For the choir of Jesus College, Cambridge

LOVE'S REDEEMING WORK IS DONE

Text: Charles Wesley (1707-1788)
Music: Malcolm Archer (b.1952)

For Robert Prizeman and St. Philip's Choir, Norbury

MY GOD AND KING

Text: George Herbert (1593-1632)
Music: Alan Viner (b.1951)

my God and King, my God and King!

The heav'ns are not too high,

his praise may thi - ther fly; the

earth is not too low, his prai - - - ses there may

Let the world in ev - 'ry cor - ner sing,

grow. Let all the world in ev - 'ry cor - ner sing,
Let all the world in ev - 'ry cor - ner sing,
Let all the world in ev - 'ry cor - ner sing,

let all the world in ev - 'ry cor - ner sing, let all the

must shout, no door can

keep them out;

but, a-bove all, the heart must

bear the long - est part.

Full Sw. (box closed)
Gt. 8' 4' add
mf

ff *marcato*

Let all the world in

ff *marcato*

cresc.

ff

f

ev - 'ry cor - ner sing, let all the world in ev - 'ry cor - ner sing,

f

my God and King. Let all the world in ev - 'ry cor - ner

sing, my God and King.

Full

In memoriam Diana, Princess of Wales

O LORD GOD OF CONSOLATION

Text: adapted from the 'Nunc Dimittis'
Music: Andrew Gant (b.1963)

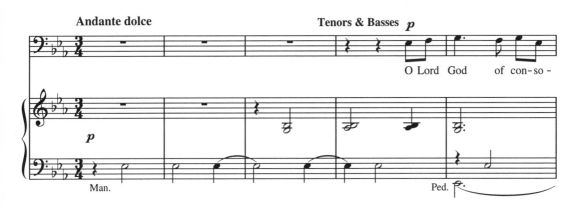

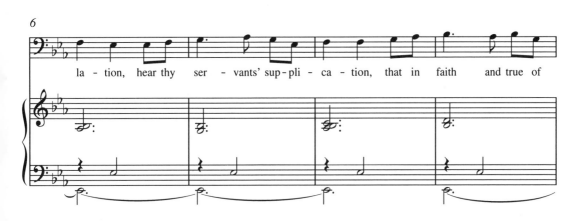

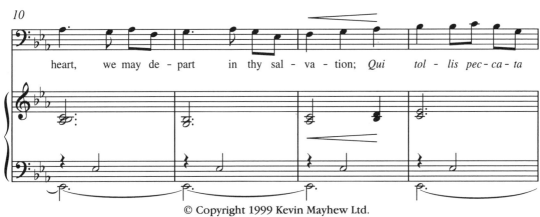

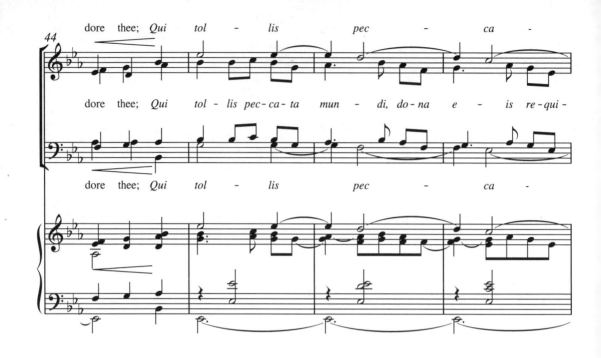

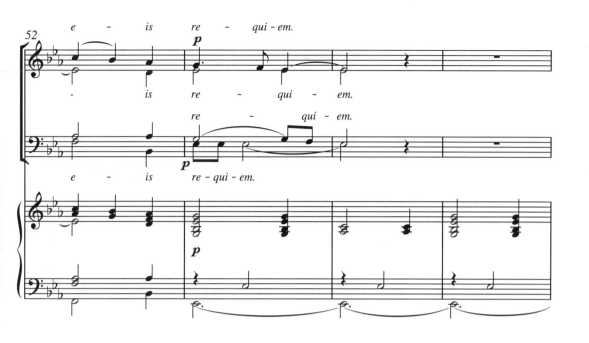

50 NEW ANTHEMS
FOR MIXED VOICES

O MAGNUM MYSTERIUM

Text: from Scripture
Music: Margaret Rizza (b.1929)

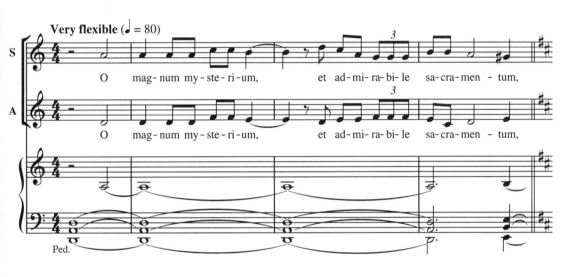

O mag-num my-ste-ri-um, et ad-mi-ra-bi-le sa-cra-men - tum,

O mag-num my-ste-ri-um, et ad-mi-ra-bi-le sa-cra-men - tum,

ut a-ni - ma-li-a vi-de-rent Do-mi-num na-tum, ja-cen-tum in prae-

ut a-ni - na-li-a vi-de-rent Do-mi-num na-tum, ja-cen-tum in prae-

O SAVIOUR OF THE WORLD

Text: Collect for the Visitation of the Sick from the 'Book of Common Prayer'
adapted by Christopher Tambling
Music: Christopher Tambling (b.1964)

us and help us, save us and help us, we

Save us and help us, save us and help us, we

Save us and help us, save us and help us, we

Save us and help us, save us and help us, we

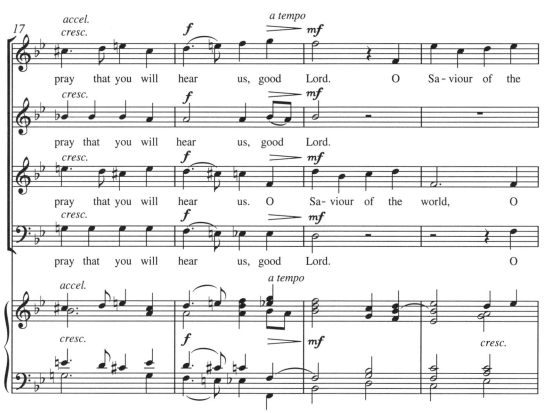

pray that you will hear us, good Lord. O Sa-viour of the

pray that you will hear us, good Lord.

pray that you will hear us. O Sa-viour of the world, O

pray that you will hear us, good Lord. O

world, O Sa-viour of the world, through your cross and pre-cious

O Sa-viour of the world, through your cross and pre-cious

Sa-viour of the world, O Sa-viour, through your cross and pre-cious

Sa-viour of the world, O Sa-viour, through your cross and pre-cious

Man.

blood you have gi-ven us new life. Save us and

blood you have gi-ven us new life. Save us and

blood you have gi-ven us new life. Save us and

blood you have gi-ven us new life. Save us and

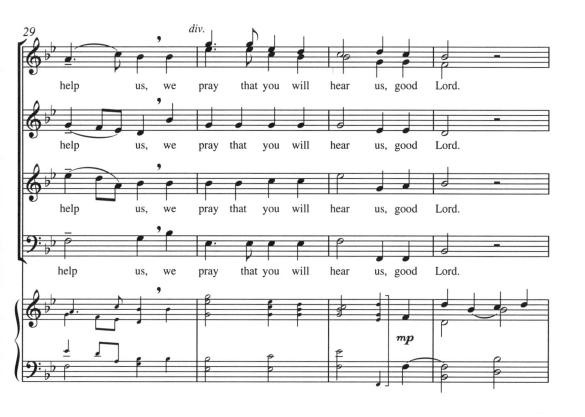

help us, we pray that you will hear us, good Lord.

help us, we pray that you will hear us, good Lord.

help us, we pray that you will hear us, good Lord.

help us, we pray that you will hear us, good Lord.

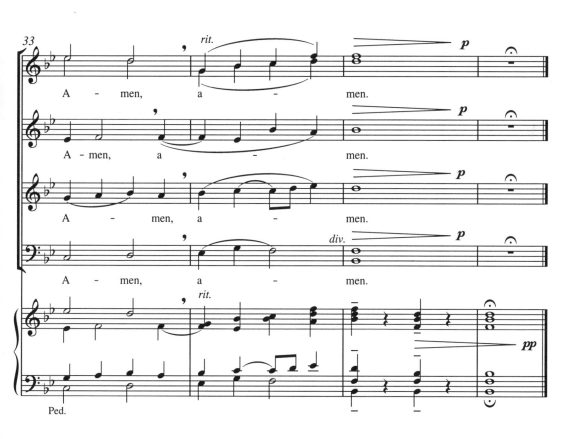

A - men, a - men.

A - men, a - men.

A - men, a - men.

A - men, a - men.

Ped.

PRAISE TO THE LORD

Text: Hubert J. Richards (b.1921), based on J. Neander and Psalm 96
Music: Richard Lloyd (b.1933)

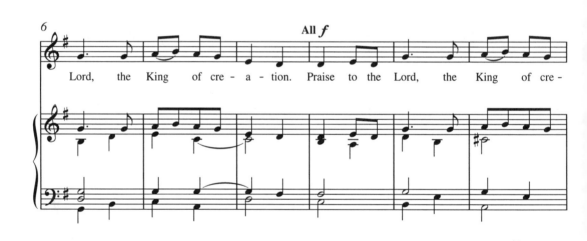

bles-sed be God for e-ver, a-men. Bles-sed be God for e-ver, a-men.

2. Come tell of his won-der-ful deeds, come,

come,

Man.

Ped.

thank him for what he has done, and of-fer your gifts to the Lord.

Bles-sed be God for e - ver, a - men. Bles-sed be God,

bles-sed be God for e - ver, a-men. Bles-sed be God for e - ver, a-men.

3. Come let all the earth shout for joy, come   come

Man.   Ped.

worship the Lord in his house, the Lord who made hea-ven and earth.

All *unis.*

Bles-sed be God for e - ver, a - men. Bles-sed be God,

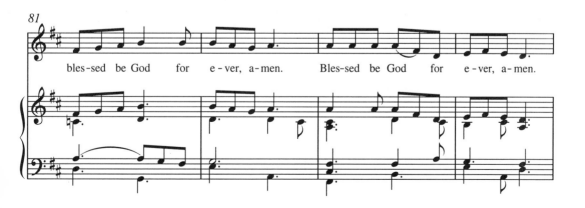

bles-sed be God for e - ver, a-men. Bles-sed be God for e - ver, a-men.

Man.

Tempo I

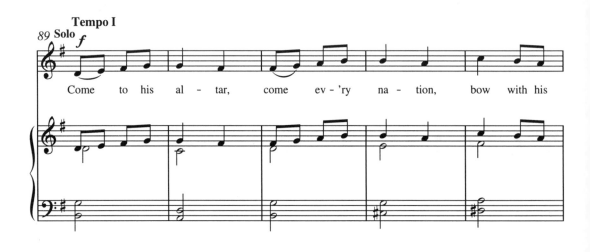

Come to his al - tar, come ev - 'ry na - tion, bow with his

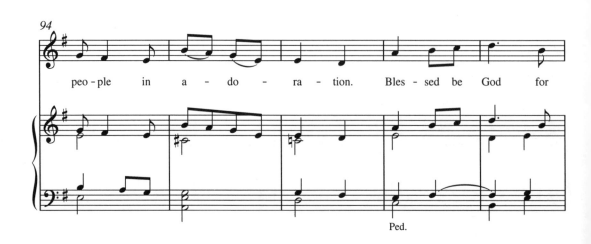

peo - ple in a - do - ra - tion. Bles - sed be God for

Ped.

PRAYER OF SERENITY

Text: Anonymous
Music: Quentin Thomas (b.1972)

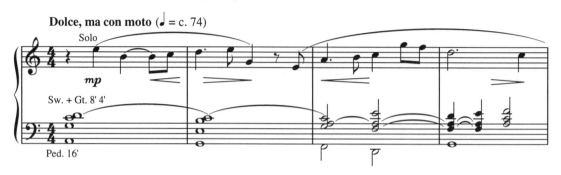

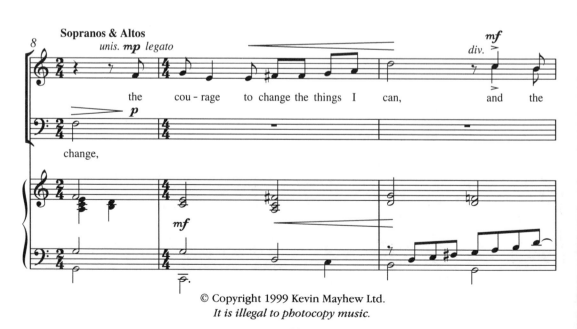

wis - dom to know the dif - f'rence. Thy will, not

mine, be done.

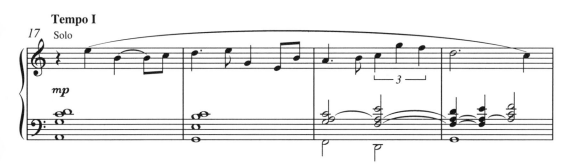

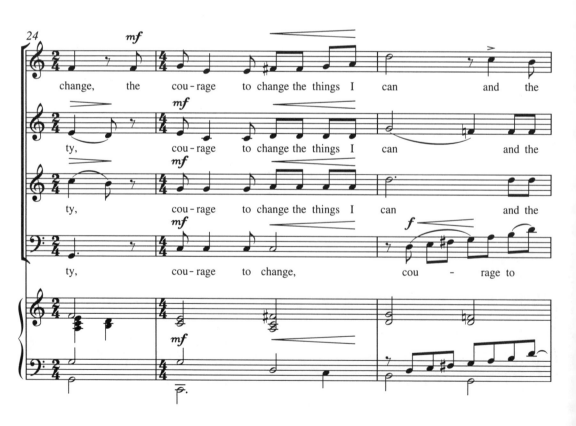

REJOICE IN THE LORD ALWAY

Text: Philippians 4:4-7
Music: Christopher Tambling (b.1964)

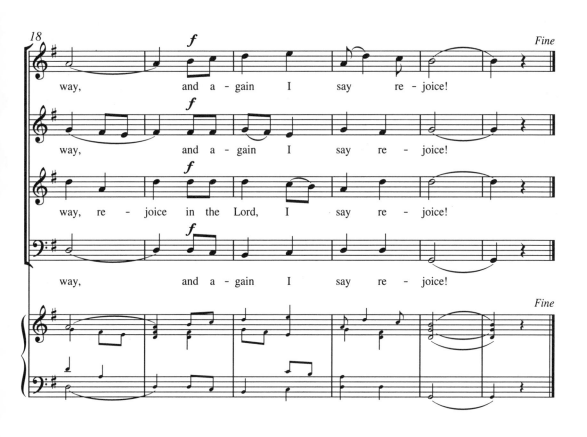

* *Original words are 'known unto all men'*

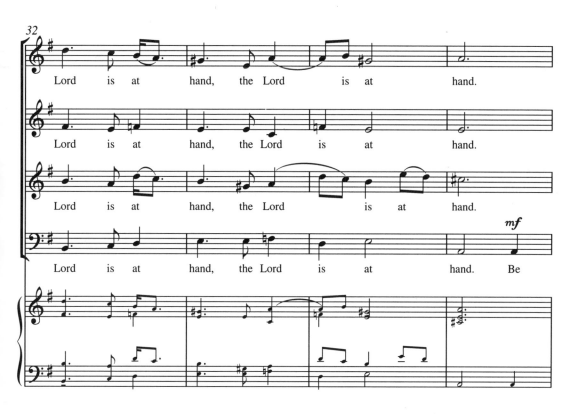

Lord is at hand, the Lord is at hand.

Lord is at hand, the Lord is at hand.

Lord is at hand, the Lord is at hand.

Lord is at hand, the Lord is at hand. Be

Be care - ful for no - thing, but in

Be care - ful for no - thing, be care - ful for no - thing, but in

Be care - ful for no - thing, but in

care - ful for no - thing, for no - thing, be care - ful for no - thing, but in

ev - 'ry-thing by prayer, by prayer and sup-pli - ca - tion let your re -

ev - 'ry-thing by prayer, by prayer and sup-pli - ca - tion let your re -

ev - 'ry-thing by prayer, by prayer and sup-pli - ca - tion let your re -

ev - 'ry-thing by prayer, by prayer and sup-pli - ca - tion let your re -

quests be known un - to God. And the peace of God, and the

quests be known un - to God. And the peace of God, and the

quests be known un - to God. And the peace of God, and the

quests be known un - to God. And the peace of God,

peace of God which pas - seth all un - der - stand - ing, shall

peace of God which pas - seth all un - der - stand - ing, shall

peace of God which pas - seth all un - der - stand - ing, shall

which pas - seth under - stand - ing, shall

D.S. al Fine

p cresc.

keep your hearts and minds through Christ Je - sus our Lord. Re -

keep your hearts and minds through Christ Je - sus our Lord.

keep your hearts and minds through Christ Je - sus our Lord.

keep your hearts and minds through Christ Je - sus our Lord.

D.S. al Fine

50 NEW ANTHEMS
FOR MIXED VOICES

SING THE LIFE

Text: Albert F. Bayly (1901-1984)
Music: William Lloyd Webber (1914-1982)

him a - dore, Lord of life for e - ver - more,

Lord of life for e - ver - more.

mp Sing the beau - ty now un - fold-ing,

ev - 'ry bud a

mp

fair in flow'r and tree;

p

pro - mise hold - ing *mf*

of more life to be.

mp *mf*

Sing the Lord who death de-fea-ted, now in ro-yal glo-ry sea-ted: with all na-ture Christ a-dore, Lord of life for e-ver-more, Lord of life for e-ver-more.

SPIRIT OF GOD

Text: Cecil Alexander (1818-1895)
Music: David Terry (b.1975)

Thou that art pow'r and peace com - bined, all high-est strength, all

pur - est love, the rush-ing of the migh - ty wind, the brood-ing of the

gen - tle dove, come, give us still thy pow'r-ful aid, and urge us on, and

keep us thine; nor leave the hearts that once were made fit tem-ples for thy

grace di - vine; nor let us quench thy sev'n - fold light; but

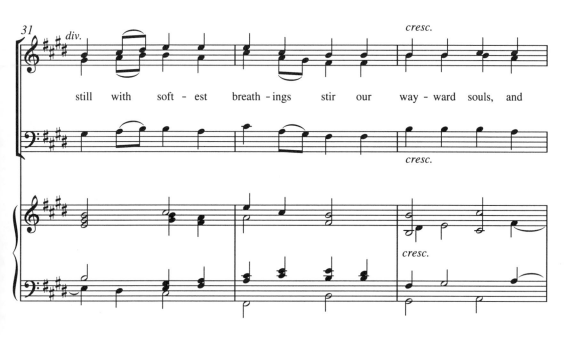

still with soft - est breath -ings stir our way - ward souls, and

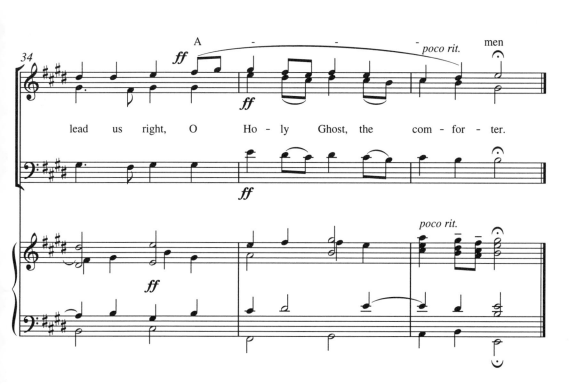

lead us right, O Ho - ly Ghost, the com - for - ter.

50 NEW ANTHEMS
FOR MIXED VOICES

TANTUM ERGO

Text: Thomas Aquinas (1227-1274)
Music: William Lloyd Webber (1914-1982)

Translation: *Such a great Sacrament; let us revere with heads bent,*
and let the Old Testament give way to the New Observance.
Let faith supply what the senses lack.

To the Father and the Son let there be praise and celebration.
Health, honour and also strength be given, as well as blessing.
To the One who proceeds from them both let equal praise be given.

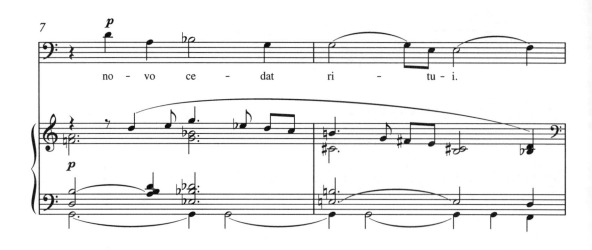

no - vo ce — dat ri — tu - i.

Prae - stet fi — des sup - ple - men - tum

Man.

sen - su - um de — fec - tu - i, sen - su - um de-

poco rit.

poco rit.

Ped.

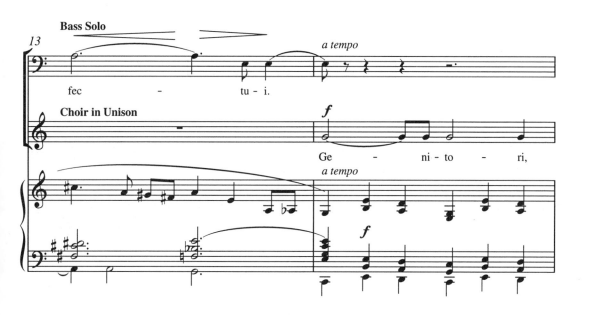

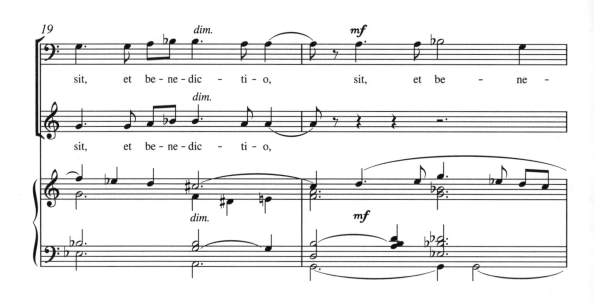

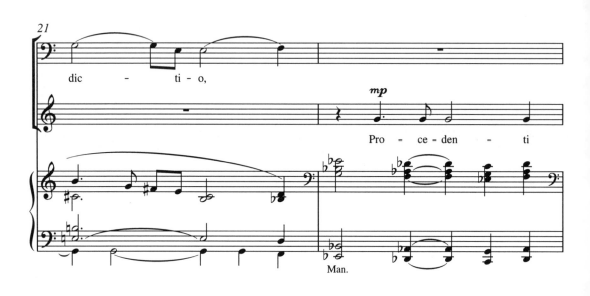

TEACH ME, MY GOD AND KING

Text: George Herbert (1593-1633)
Music: Michael Rose (b.1934)

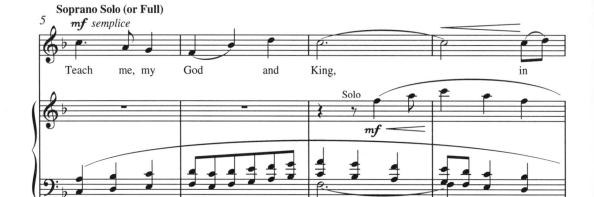

on it may stay his eye; or if he plea - seth, through it pass, and then the heav'ns e - spy.

All voices

All

Man.

may of thee par - take;

Add *mf*

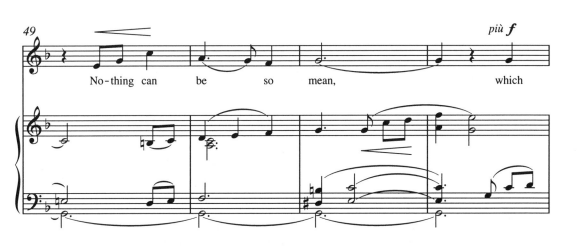

No-thing can be so mean, which

più f

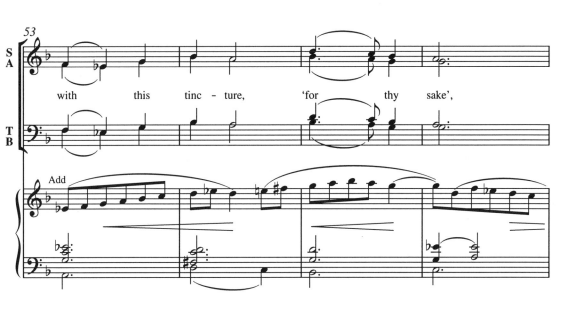

with this tinc - ture, 'for thy sake',

Add

will not grow   bright   and clean.

A ser - vant   with   this

A ser - vant   with   this

A ser - vant   with   this

A ser -   vant   with   this

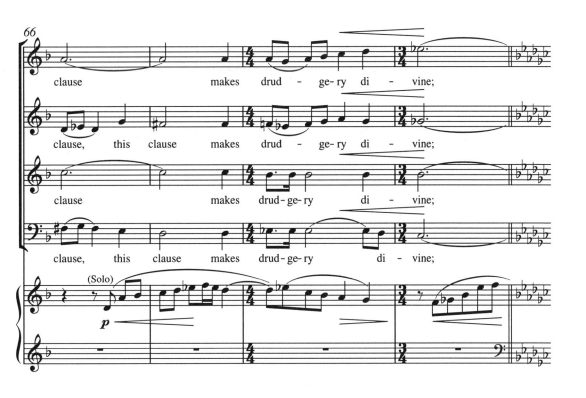

clause   makes   drud - ge-ry di - vine;

clause,   this   clause   makes   drud - ge-ry di - vine;

clause   makes   drud-ge-ry   di - vine;

clause,   this   clause   makes   drud-ge-ry   di - vine;

(Solo)

p

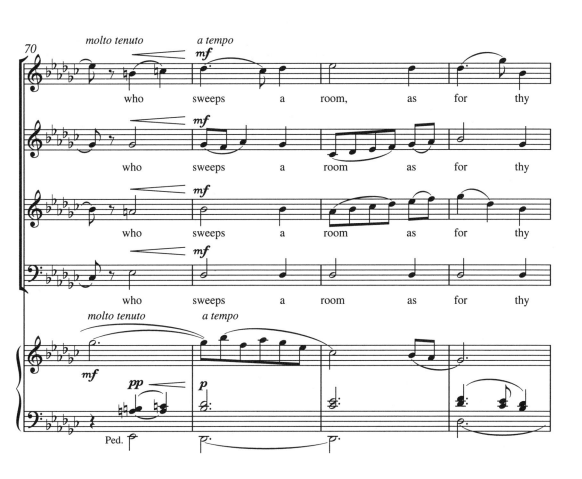

molto tenuto   *a tempo*

mf

who   sweeps   a   room,   as   for   thy

mf

who   sweeps   a   room   as   for   thy

mf

who   sweeps   a   room   as   for   thy

mf

who   sweeps   a   room   as   for   thy

molto tenuto   *a tempo*

mf

pp   *p*

Ped. *p*   *p.*   *p.*

laws,   makes   that   and the   ac - tion   fine.

laws,   makes   that   and the   ac – tion   fine.

laws,   makes   that   and the   ac – tion   fine.

laws,   makes   that   and the   ac – tion   fine.

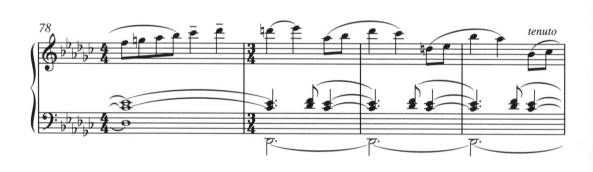

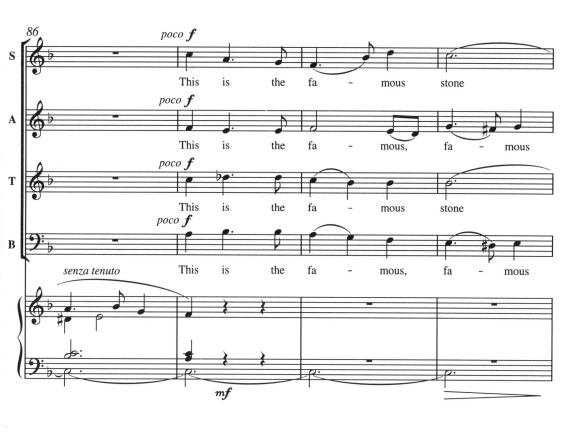

237

for that which God doth touch and

for that which God doth touch and

for that which God doth touch and

gold; for that which God doth touch and

own can - not for less be told.

own can - not for less be told, be told.

own can - not for less be told.

own can - not for less be told.

Can - not for less be told.

Can - not for less be told.

Can - not for less be told.

Can - not for less be told.

* Tenor divisi if no Bass I available

239

50 NEW ANTHEMS
FOR MIXED VOICES

For Susie and Robin

THE GRACE OF CHRIST

Text: John Newton (1725-1807)
Music: Richard Lloyd (b.1933)

THE GRAIL PRAYER

Text: Traditional Prayer
Music: Margaret Rizza (b.1929)

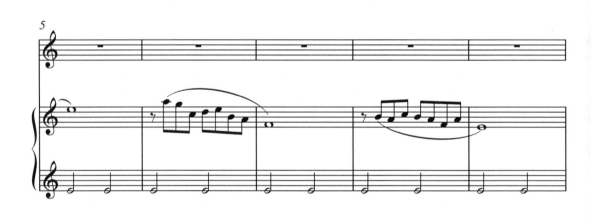

Lord Jesus, I give you my hands to do your work;

words; I give you my mind, Lord, that you may think in me; I give you my

spi - rit, that you may pray in me, that you may pray in me.

Soprano Solo or Semi-chorus

A- bove all, Lord, I give you my heart, that you may

Ah, (or Hum)

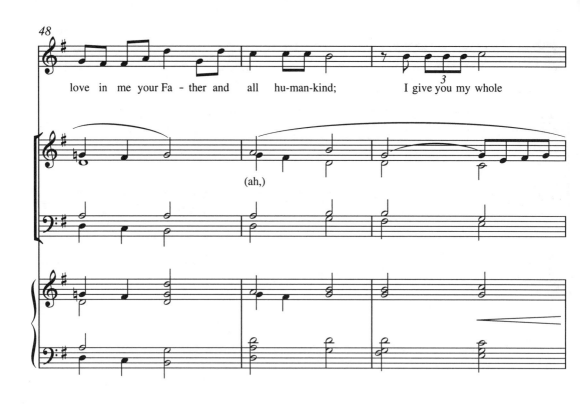

love in me your Fa - ther and all hu-man-kind; I give you my whole

(ah,)

self that you may grow in me, so that it is you, Lord Je - sus, who

(ah,)

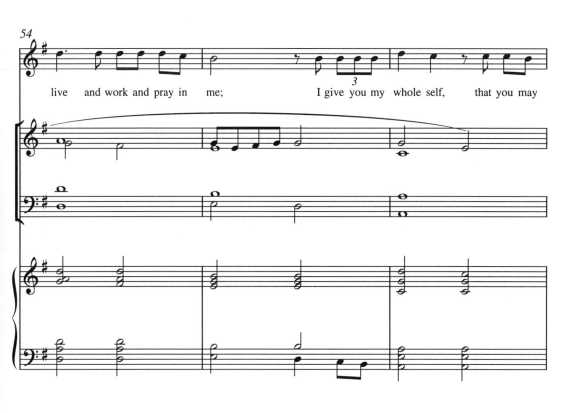

live and work and pray in me; I give you my whole self, that you may

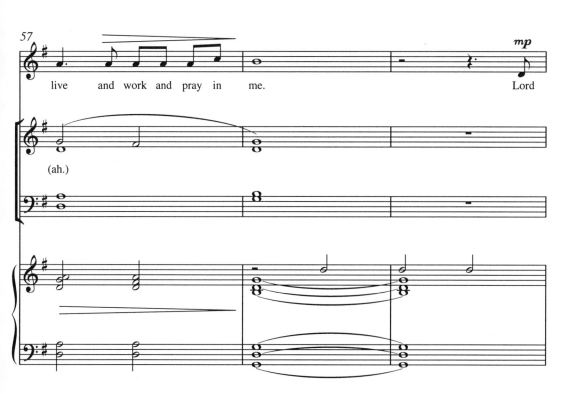

live and work and pray in me. Lord

(ah.)

Je - sus, I give you my spi-rit, that you may

Hum

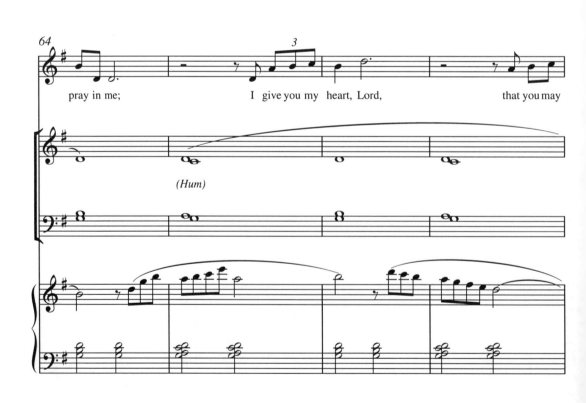

pray in me; I give you my heart, Lord, that you may

(Hum)

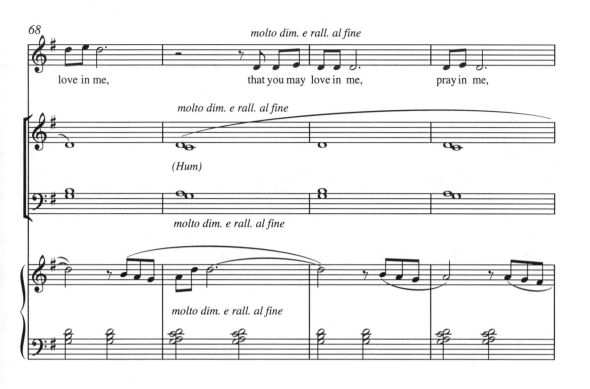

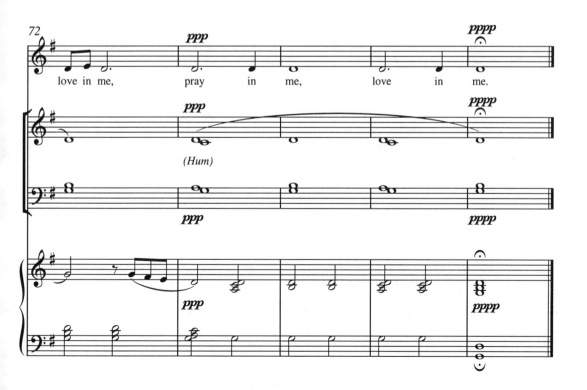

249

For Katy and Paul

THE GREATEST OF THESE

Text: Christopher Wordsworth (1807-1885)
Music: Richard Lloyd (b.1933)

Love is kind and suf - fers long, love is

meek and thinks no wrong, love than death it -

self more strong; there - fore give us love.

Faith will va - nish in - to sight; hope be

Faith will va - nish, hope

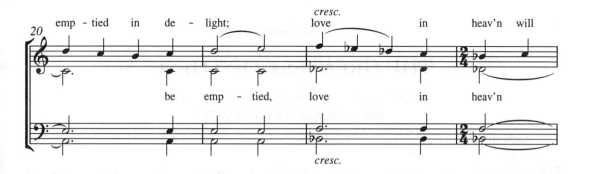

THE LORD BLESS YOU AND KEEP YOU

Text: Numbers 6:24
Music: Andrew Wright (b.1950)

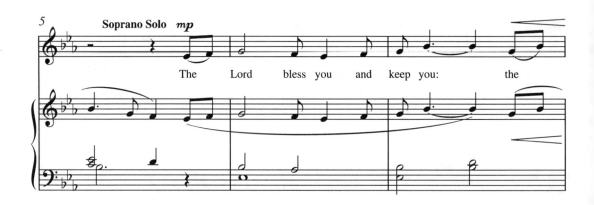

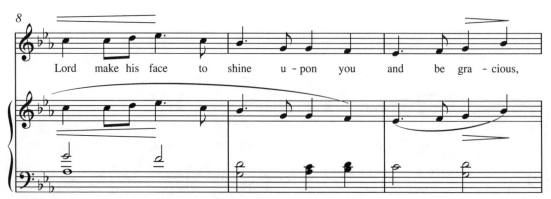

This anthem may also be sung unaccompanied.

50 NEW ANTHEMS
FOR MIXED VOICES

THE LORD IS MY SHEPHERD

Text: Psalm 23
Music: Colin Mawby (b.1936)

fear. You are there with your crook and your staff,

with your crook and your staff; with these you give me

com - fort. You have pre - pared a ban - quet for me

Man.

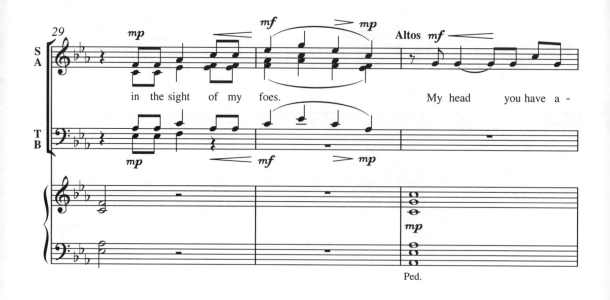

in the sight of my foes. My head you have a-

noin - ted with oil;

Tenors & Basses *unis.* *p*

My cup is o - ver - flow - ing.

Sopranos *p*

Sure - ly good-ness and kind - ness shall fol - low me

Man.

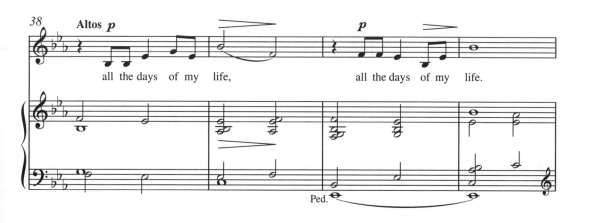

all the days of my life, all the days of my life.

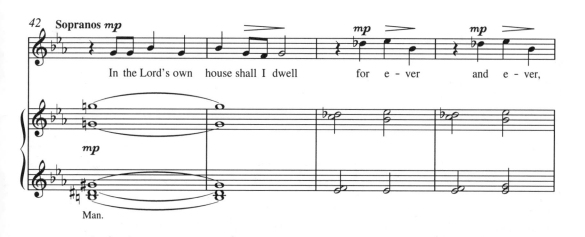

In the Lord's own house shall I dwell for e - ver and e - ver,

Man.

for e - ver and e - ver, for e - ver and e - ver.

Ped.

Dedicated to Professor Peter Toyne and first performed in Liverpool Cathedral
at the inaugural service of John Moores University, Liverpool, 26th September 1992

THE TRUE GLORY

Text: Prayer of Sir Francis Drake (c.1540-1596)
Music: Noel Rawsthorne (b.1929)

dea-vour in a-ny great mat-ter, grant us al-so to know that it is not the be-gin-ning, but the con-ti-nu-ing of the same un-til it be tho-rough-ly

263

fi - nish'd.

Poco meno mosso

The

grea - test things are ac - com - plish'd,

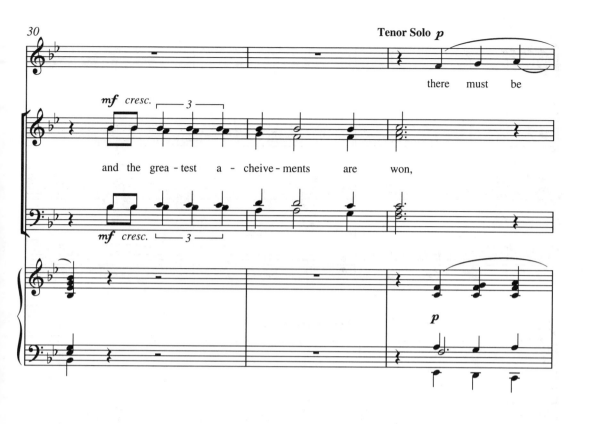

yields the true glo - ry.

yields the true glo - ry.

yields the true glo - ry.

yields the true glo - ry.

TIMELESS LOVE

Text: Timothy Dudley-Smith (b.1926) based on Psalm 89
Music: Norman Warren (b.1934)

glory, love more firm than an-cient earth. Tell his faith - ful-ness a-
found - ed, skies and seas de-clare his name. Wind and storm o-bey his

broad, who is like him, praise the Lord!
word,